GOING THERE

Patient Centred Consulting for GPs and Patients

'Patient Centred'? What's that all about?

We look at what happens in a patient's life before they come to the doctor. This is being 'Patient Centred'.

Stories by Peter Worrall, Bevis Heap and Fieza Chaudry

Illustrations by Lucy Andrews

Matador
9 Priory Business Park,
Wistow Road, Kibworth Beauchamp,
Leicestershire. LE8 0RX
Tel: 0116 279 2299
Email: books@troubador.co.uk
Web: www.troubador.co.uk/matador
Twitter: @matadorbooks

ISBN 978 1800461 253

British Library Cataloguing in Publication Data.
A catalogue record for this book is available from the British Library.

Printed and bound by CPI Group (UK) Ltd, Croydon, CR0 4YY
Typeset in 11pt Gill Sans Nova by Troubador Publishing Ltd, Leicester, UK

Matador is an imprint of Troubador Publishing Ltd

FOREWORD

Centuries ago only priests were permitted to read the Bible. Even then, to help 'common people' read it was forbidden. Similarly, early NHS prescriptions had a tick-box so doctors could advise pharmacists whether or not to name the medication; this to avoid unnecessary patient concern. GPs no longer have a priestly role as the patriarchal holders and imparters of medical knowledge. Patients also have access to information, even if it is inaccurate or unsafe for them to follow. Doctors are now the interpreters and clarifiers. To do this effectively they need to explore and incorporate aspects of patient 'lifeworld', so adding to the 'ideas, concerns and expectations' they have been assimilating for years.

Once the GP understands the patient's current knowledge and beliefs and circumstances, they can discuss what should happen next, by sharing uncertainties and alternatives if things don't happen as expected; sometimes way beyond the safety of clinical knowledge.

Graphic novels are gaining credence. They can add powerfully to quiet reflective practice, thus complementing the daily world of words. Not only that, 'Going There' illustrates patient-centred consulting in a manner suitable for RCGP assessment and introduces patients to current practice. So let's enjoy it – It's a fun read.

Professor Simon Gregory DL, Deputy Medical Director, Primary and Integrated Care, Health Education England, GP, King Edward Road Surgery, Northampton

AUTHORS

Peter Worrall started his career in education as an RAF Education Officer and ended up as principal of a multicultural community school in Leicester. On retirement he worked as an OU tutor and became involved in medical training in Leicester, developing a team of simulated patients (SPs) to work on communication skills with medical students and GP registrars. Interestingly, it was during this period that patient-centredness moved from being a voluntary element in 'good practice' to an assessed element of RCGP requirements – an era of new learning for Peter.

Dr Bevis Heap was born and brought up in Yorkshire and qualified from Leicester in 1981. He has worked in and around Leicestershire since then. He was a GP for more than 29 years, retiring from practice in July 2015. A GP trainer for over 26 years he has been involved in the New Trainers Courses, for what is now Health Education England, working across the East Midlands for some years. He is also an Associate Postgraduate Dean in HEE and has a portfolio of jobs there. When not working in health care, he enjoys his family, railway modelling and DIY.

Dr Fieza Chaudry was born and raised in Leicester. Her medical career began in her home town, where she graduated in 2009 and completed her GP training in 2014. Working as a salaried GP, she developed an interest in medical teaching and became a GP trainer in 2015. She recently moved to practise in London and hopes to pursue her passion for teaching there. Outside of work she is a keen traveller and loves to bake.

Lucy Andrews – A Leicester-based illustrator and ceramicist with a BA in Design Crafts and an MA in Museum Studies. Lucy works from her studio at Two Queens in Leicester's Cultural Centre. This project has been her largest illustrative commission to date.

ACKNOWLEDGEMENTS

We would like to express our gratitude to Dr Sue Hadley, Dr Rhona Knight and Dr Nigel Scarborough for their initial scrutiny and encouragements.

ABBREVIATIONS USED IN THIS BOOK

Doctors use many abbreviations to make their conversations shorter. Some of these may be familiar; others less so, so here's a list of the ones we've used in this book in the order they first appear.

TIA: Transient Ischaemic attack or Mini-stroke as it is sometimes known.

ICE: Ideas, concerns and expectations.

CSR: Clinical Supervisor's Report (this is part of the evidence collected in a GP Registrar's Training.

e-Portfolio: an electronic portfolio the Registrar records learning on and collects evidence towards their qualification for General Practice.

ED: Emergency Department (A&E).

A&E: Accident and Emergency Department.

CSA: Clinical Skills Assessment. A simulated surgery which is done in London at the Royal College of GPs as part of the assessments of a Registrar's progress to becoming a fully fledged GP.

Author's note: just as we were preparing this book for publication, the CSA was suspended for Covid-19. It has been replaced, at least for the time being, by the Recorded Consultation Analysis (RCA). The competencies to be demonstrated in the RCA are essentially the same.

ICEE: See above with effects added to ensure the management proposed by the GP is appropriate to the particular patient.

CXR: Chest x-ray.

UTI: Urinary Tract Infection otherwise known as a water infection.

SPs: Simulated Patients. People who can replicate the same patient's problem to different doctors.

IHD: Ischaemic Heart Disease, problems with the blood supply to the heart leading to problems such as angina or a Heart Attack.

BP: Blood Pressure.

COT: Consultation Observation Tool. An assessment of a consultation where the GP Trainer either sits in or watches a video.

CEX: Clinical Evaluation Exercise. Similar to a COT but done in hospital placements.

ARCP: Annual Review of Competency Panel. An annual review of the evidence of the Registrar's e-Portfolio.

ALOBA: Agenda Led Outcome Based Analysis. A way of looking at a consultation.

VTS: Vocational Training Scheme. An older term for the Whole Day Release where training takes place out of the GP practice.

CRENA: Explained in the text!

TATT: Tired all the time.

NSAIDs: Non-Steroidal Anti-inflammatories. Drugs like Ibuprofen.

ST: Speciality Trainee.

ESR: Educational Supervisor's Report. A review of the Registrar's training.

CBT: Cognitive Behaviour Therapy. A method of managing anxiety and other mental health issues.

AKT: Applied Knowledge Test. A computerised assessment of the doctor's ability to use their knowledge.

GMC: General Medical Council. The governance body for doctors in the UK.

HbA1c: A blood test that shows how well your body has been dealing with blood sugars over the last 2–3 months.

CBD: Another assessment of the registrar which looks in depth at their knowledge and approach to some aspects of a case.

WDR: See VTS above.

RHS: Not a medical one! Royal Horticultural Society.

'GOING THERE'

The phrase 'Going There' was extracted from a GP training feedback session. Dr Jane, a registrar, had seen the distressed mother of a 14 year old girl, Emma, who refused to go to school. Her widowed mother with other children to care for couldn't understand her behaviour because she was doing well academically at school. Emma simply sat facing Dr Jane in silence, making no eye contact. *'It was then'*, she told us, *'I knew I had to go there – to get behind Emma's silence'*. Mother quickly agreed Emma could come alone. The next day the two sat there looking at each other. Quietly, Dr J asked, *what was happening at school?* Immediately, she burst into tears! Apparently, her close group of friends often spoke of family activity which to Emma always seemed to revolve around their fathers. More tears! It transpired Emma had lost her father when she was 12 – somehow or another she'd had no opportunity to grieve. She'd kept thinking about him and suffering from flashbacks.

'Going There' enabled Dr J to incorporate that part of Emma's life into her treatment. And, subsequently, her repeat appointments became a cherished part of her life.

We've got to get Laurie down

RING RING

Tracy? Can you pop round? I'm worried about Dad.

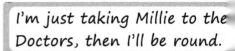

I'm just taking Millie to the Doctors, then I'll be round.

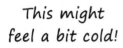

8

Aisha, this is Martine. She's training to be a trainer. You might want to sit in with her this afternoon? Could be useful for both of you.

This is Pratika, our new pharmacist. New in both senses; we've never had an on-site pharmacist before.

11

12

To be Patient Centred we incorporate our clinical experience with health aspects of each patient's "lifeworld", curiously referred to as the holistic approach; more mundanely we call it "going there".

'Holistic medicine is really just good medicine. It means caring for the whole child in the context of that child's values, their family's beliefs, their family system, and their culture in the larger community, and considering a range of therapies based on the evidence of their benefits and cost.'

Kemper, K. J., (2000) 'Holistic Pediatrics = good medicine', Pediatrics, 105(1). p. S214.

'Holistic care can be interpreted only in relation to an individual perception of holism. This means that even if you offer the same health advice, therapies and interventions, they will have different meanings to different people. This view acknowledges objective scientific explanations of physiology but also admits that people have inner experiences that are subjective, mystical and, for some religious, which may also affect their health and well-being.'

Royal College of General Practitioners (2019)
The RCGP Curriculum: Being a General Practitioner.
https://www.rcgp.org.uk/-/media/Files/GP-training-and-exams
Curriculum-2019/RCGPJ7408-Being-A-GP-Curriculum-WEB
-v21910.pdf (Accessed 11/05/20). p. 82.

Mr Carter, tell me, what's the problem?

She made me come!

Something scary happened at work! He needed rescuing

Sounds dramatic! What happened?

I was in my crane cab and suddenly I couldn't see anything... I couldn't get to the radio with my right hand. Next thing I know I'm being lowered to the ground, an ambulance waiting...

What's going on here? A TIA? How would I sort that out?

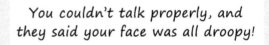

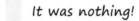

You seem reluctant to be here. What are you really worried about Laurie?

I wouldn't have asked about ICE straight out...

Well, I heard them say something about not being able to work...?

OK, so you've had a short time when your speech wasn't right, vision was weird and your arm didn't work, which led to your rescue. You feel fine now but you're worried about work. Jan's concerned it's a stroke. Does that about sum it up?

Yeah, I suppose so.

Let's go behind the screen. I'll examine your blood pressure, listen to neck arteries, assess strength in your arms, legs and reflexes.

Fine.

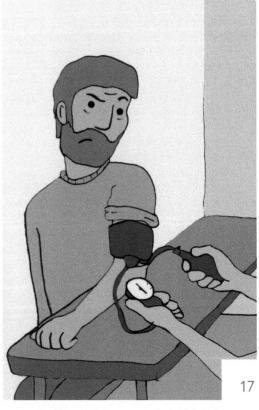

Everything seems fine **now**, but Jan's right, what you had sounds like a TIA or mini-stroke.

It needs more investigation and medicine to reduce further ris That's not what you were expecting me to say, was it

Jan's been fussing and winding up the family

And there's another bit of bad news...

Until we decide what this was you have to stop driving. If it's a TIA, then you can't drive for a month.

No chance!

Sorry Laurie, I'm not being awkward, but it's the law. Drive and your insurance will be void and you could wind up in court.

And there's more. Work won't want you back for a while. They can't risk another episode...

This just gets better and better! ...I suppose I don't have any other options, do I?

No, you haven't. We're all trying to help.

OK, to action. Start the medication and I'd like to see you in a couple of weeks. Not good news, but we've covered a lot.

Thanks Doctor.

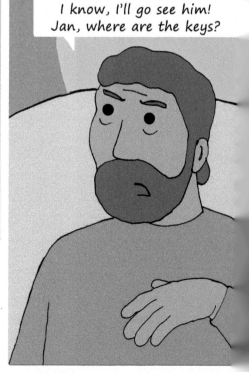

20

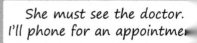

AAAAHH!!!
AAAHH!!
It's something in Madge's garden!
HELP!
Laurie quick! Madge needs help!

24

So to encourage patients to take the lead we greet amiably and listen. Amongst ourselves we call it starting anywhere and there we are, dealing with our joint priorities.

And for me, it was straight into 'what do I do next?'. Now I'm beginning to feel more comfortable – each patient is so different.

'Patient centred care is best delivered in relationships that foster shared decision making: an approach that has been shown to encourage health promoting behaviours, reduce inappropriate care, and improve patient and doctor satisfaction – Why doctors need to include patients in their diagnoses.'

Berger, Z. D. et al (2017) Patient centred diagnosis: sharing diagnostic decisions with patients in clinical practice', BMJ, 359. p. j4218

So, welcome to Jupiter Road! Let's catch up. You've completed 4 months General Medicine and 4 months Paediatrics. Have you had the CSR for the paeds job yet?

Should be on the e-Portfolio. ...Yes, here it is.

How do you feel about your experiences?

Scary to start with, but now I think I can manage to deal with a sick child.

So, where next? 4 months wit us, then back to hospital for E (A&E) and Psychiatry with a stint at Market Stre in between.

THEN back to us for you last year. Lo like a lot bu it'll soon pas

I'm not looking forward to CSA.

We'll start gently and build up. It'll be a tussle between new experience your confidence. Until you can sit there and work with the patient 'uncluttered' with all this training stuff (frameworks)... Let's ha a coffee break!

Yes! Tea for me please.

We'll start with 'feedback'. You have observed me in Pendleton style, what did I do well?

I thought debriefs were about you observing me!

True, but let's do it the other way round. It applies to us all, doesn't it? And you can still put any learning in your e-Portfolio.

Mmm, what do I think you did well?

Well, you made a diagnosis, got him on treatment and referred him.

OK, how did I do that?

Though it was obvious he didn't want to be here, you got him to talk and you got him to express his concerns for ICE without asking him directly, as I would have done.

s, doing this conversationally is best d it's good to consider an extra **E** - Effects. Let's set that as your first k – elicit ICEE conversationally and to do it the first minutes.

How about how I greeted them?

Quite formally to start, and then 'What are we doing today?'. Most GPs say 'what can I do for you?'

s, but 'what can I do?' is a big power statement and we want to share not y the clinical facts but the effect the illness is having and any important otional issues. at's a biggy 't it?

I remember Martine used a different greeting with each patient.

I also noticed at the end you didn't say he must do things, you suggested and explained what might happen if he didn't.

31

The family will make sure he does though. Mrs Carter will make sure he does the right thing, as will his daughter.

She was our patient before she moved. It helps to know the family.

It's so much more complicated than seeing patients in a clinic! There are a few things I need to think about for my log-entry.

Let's agree to focus on the big E (ICEE) for your next full surgery.

We'll book six then I'll pop in for a debrief.

OK.

Hello? Right, on my way.

It's nearly dinner time at school and they need me. You had better have a smile by the time I get back!

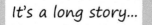

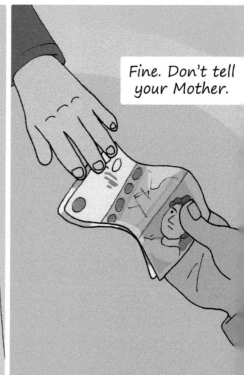

So, let's have a look at who you've seen...

Mr Pearson. What did you find with him?

He came in wanting antibiotics for a sore throat, and said it'd helped his two day sore throat before. He didn't look ill, not life affecting, BUT I did give in. He was so so so insistent!

Remind me, we should have a tutorial on the Guidelines and Iceberg Health Care Model so you can manage this without having to give in.

Who's next?

Mrs B. She came in with a cough, was worried about cancer and requested a CXR after seeing the TV adverts. Realised I didn't have to work out ICE as she's already told me. She'd got upset when I did; said I hadn't listened. I did ask effects (E) though. There were none except being worried.

So think how could you do it differently next time?

This was a nice easy one, just asked for a repeat prescription. I didn't know why she needed to come in though. Then she asked about what happened with Mr Carter. I didn't know what to say, so I didn't.

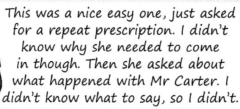

That's right, excellent, though she's his mother in law, confidentiality says she shouldn't be told any-thing without his OK.

A child with leg pain, Peter Jackson. This was difficult 'cos Mum has researched it so well and knew far more than me about things like vitamin D deficiency. So I was glad you helped me out there.

Ah yes, 'Expert Patients', someone who knows more than you on some subjects. Best to admit that and call them back if you find out a more insightful answer.

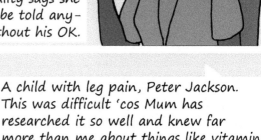

There's a whole new thing about patient 'health literacy' we'll come back to later.

How can people trust us if we don't appear to know things?

Wouldn't you trust someone more if they said they'd look it up, rather than give wrong information?

Mr Chauhan is a man with back pain who wanted a scan. I asked the usual, for how long and how painful, while I thought, doesn't sound that serious. So I went through reasons for and against a scan and whether he'd thought about physio. He chose physio. Bingo! Glad you're smiling!

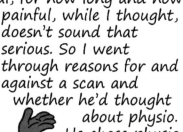

This was a 50-year-old woman with varicose veins who I phoned you to ask about a referral.

Glad you did. A good example for me of how the picture in the referral guidelines shows this would be classed as cosmetic and not referable.

Bet she wasn't happy, but we're dealing with a finite resource.

That's Mr Gartree who came in with a newspaper article on the new cholesterol drug.

Interesting the article makes it out to be a perfect drug when it's not even been fully tested. So we don't know if it's safe or not given research on only a hundred patients. I explained we couldn't prescribe a drug on the basis of a twelve week trial with only a hundred patients.

Yes, evidence based medicine, the evidence has to be enough and relevant.

41

This patient requested something to help with sleep. Her idea was tablets, but I thought we should try sleep hygiene first so gave a leaflet on that.

Ok, good not to rush to sleeping tablets with all the problems they can have but what was behind the sleep problem?

Oh, I didn't go into that. I think I should have as the patient left looking disgruntled.

Ah yes, this was Madge Moorhouse dragged in reluctantly by Mrs Carter from next door. Seemed very confused. Turned out it was a UTI.

What did I do well? Can't answer that, but I have sussed that what I labelled as complexity is all about sharing with patients and that complexity gets really interesting – different every time!

'An example of a complex issue is that of raising a child. Success in raising one child is no success in raising another'

Plsek, P. (2003) 'Complexity and the adoption of innovation in Health Care', National Committee for Quality in Health Care Conference Report. Washington DC, 27–28 January. National Committee for Health Care Management Foundation. p. 1.

'As soon as you have to interact and converse with another human, we enter a convoluted world of judgement, interpretation, facts, attitudes, beliefs, understanding, opinions, agendas, intelligence, selfishness, education, ego, power, assumption, control, desires, attitudes, needs and focus, to name but a few reasons.'

Radford, R. and Johnson, S. (2015) NHS don't kill me! Kibworth Beauchamp: Matador Publishing. p. 41.

45

OK, here's some practical points for the small group work this afternoon: Treat the SP as a real patient. Don't be afraid to try things out; making mistakes is one way to learn.

If you get stuck go time out.

Learn by watching colleagues and record what you see as evidence.

Here are today's simulated patients.

We will split you into six groups of eight or so, and you'll stay in the same room to work with three patients before a final time for reflection.

Let's go!

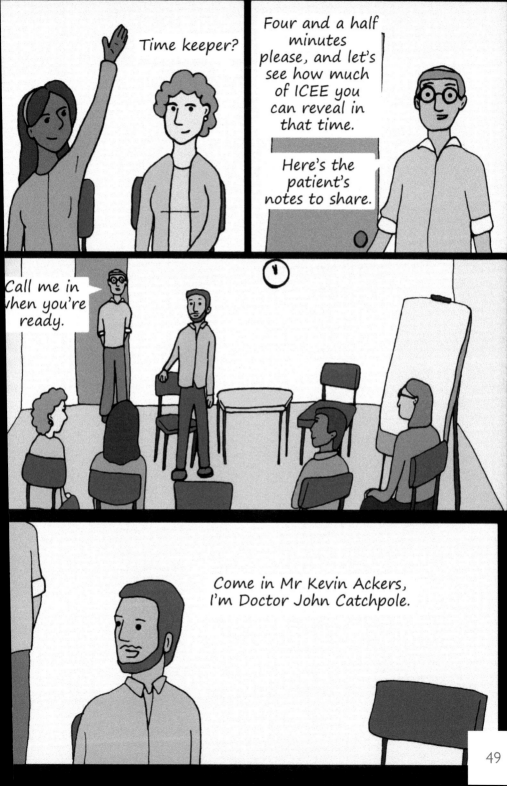

I think I got his ideas in the time available.

What did you record?

Let's see what might be missing.

I noticed your expression change when you said your husband was away a lot. Do you mind if I ask some specific questions?

MEANWHILE, GROUP 3.

...so then I had to have this lumber punch up!

?!

55

'Reflection can make medicine more enjoyable, provide more job satisfaction, and give more meaning to one's work. It can make the difference between repeating one's style of work over and over again, or each year of work building on the last, providing the basis for interesting and stimulating learning.'

Wilson, H. and Cunningham, W. (2014) Being a doctor: understanding medical practice.
London: Royal College of General Practitioners. p. 181.

59

60

Oh quite a while.

She's usually coped...

I didn't think much about it...

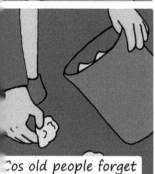

'Cos old people forget things, don't they?

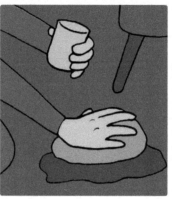

Hmmm...

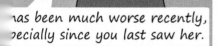

...has been much worse recently, ...pecially since you last saw her.

She's needed bringing home from the shops when she forgot where home was and it's only round the corner. And she used to keep this place really tidy.

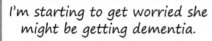

63

64

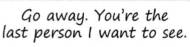

No, everything is just dandy. When's your next bus?

I think it's better if I come with you and explain.

I knew something like this would happen.

I really empathise with Jan, but she's got to live through it — at least I've been trained to cope.

Three dramas, plus Madge! What next? Not sure I can cope.

'Empathy — our ability to include another's experience into our own — is a fundamental human capacity, one that is important to the healthy functioning of friendships, family structures, societies and our earth.'

Halifax, J. (2018) Standing at the Edge: finding freedom where fear and courage meet. New York: Flatiron Books. p. 56.

Today's joint surgery, let's do a COT.

We've got to do at least six of these in combination with your hospital mini CEXs.

But that's a minimum, and in addition to the evidence you're collecting for your end of year ARCP.

Glad it's you not me!

Fine. Eight patients this morning and now I'm down to fifteen minutes per appointment.

Well, let's see who's on the list and I'll give you feedback at least, and do a COT if a case has enough interest to meet the COT criteria.

That was an eventful morning, lots of challenging cases – Let's do the COT first, I think the patient with the sleep problem is a good one.

We can talk about the other cases later, especially Frank as I know you've said you want to talk about him.

So, looking at the form, how should we score these competencies?

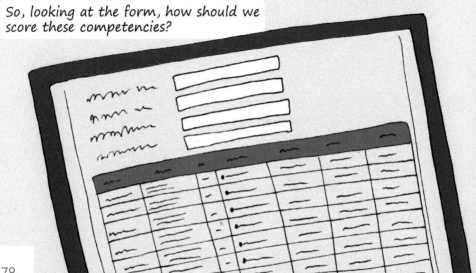

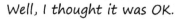

79

So overall I think that was a good case and well done. I know it's overall "needs further development", but as I've said one area was competent already.

And then there's Frank needing his letter for court after assault charges.

Yes. I was stuck to start with, but once I asked him to tell me more about why he needed it, things opened up. Made sense of growing up tensions with Laurie and Jan too.

An insight for me too, hadn't realised he felt so inadequate being skinny, never even thought of it to be honest.

I didn't think of steroid use when he said about the letter for the assault case. I had to force him to tell me why a letter was needed.

Hmm, yes, bit like getting blood out of a stone. You worked hard to get his confidence and later he opened up more about feeling inadequate and weedy compared to his mates.

Good example of 'going there'.

When we shared thoughts, we didn't think a letter was going to help.

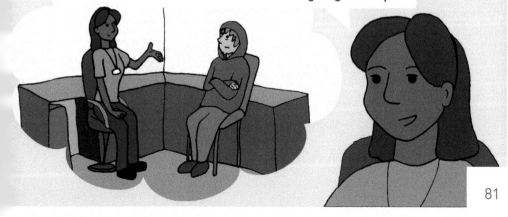

I remembered talking about getting the lawyer to write us an outline of exactly what the court would want, otherwise we might waste our time and patient's money, I used that to get him to tell me more clearly about what was going on. All that stuff about getting into debt over the drugs and getting angry for no reason.

He obviously hadn't realised the anger was to do with the steroids.

Did I go there? The big E - took much longer than 15 minutes.

It's going to be difficult for him and his family with all the other stuff going on.

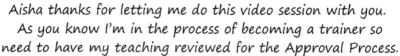

Ah it's something someone mentioned on the course. Once you've done CEE what do you do with it? C is for choices, R is for risks, E is for evidence, N is for negotiation and A is for agreement.

That makes sense. I must try and remember that.

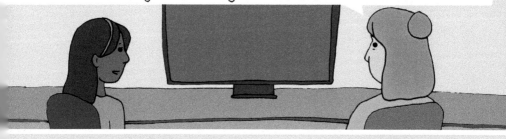

Well, let's look at a consultation on the video you did last week and see if you've done any of it without even knowing the mnemonic. Have you one in mind and do you want to give me an outline before or after?

I had five consultations recorded with appropriate consent, but I think Gran would be a good one. I'll tell you about it now. She came with her arthritis and I thought I'd done a good job on the ICEE, but I'm not sure about the rest.

Great, let's have a look.

Interesting, how do you feel after watching how you interacted with Gran?

Feels OK, thought we'd covered a lot and in a short time, felt I might have reached some agreement?

So what particular aspect of Patient Centredness would you like to explore?

Now you've mentioned CRENA, that seems a good place to start.

OK.

So I'd found out the effects of her arthritis...

...She wanted to be more active to help Jan and the family especially as she's got Frank living with her.

...And Tracy's needing child care for Millie as J. can't do it needing to wo

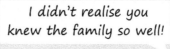
I didn't realise you knew the family so well!

They've been people I've seen quite a bit in the last three and a half months.

...aurie's problem in the crane...

Jan's been in with TATT as well, but I think that's 'cos she's got so much on her plate.

Sorry I've broken your train of thought on the video.

Having done the second E we talked about the **C**hoices and **R**isks of doing nothing, taking paracetamol or NSAIDs, physio and exercise or even surgery if things get alot worse. Maybe not so much about surgery as that's not really on as yet.

OK, what about <u>E</u>–<u>N</u>–<u>A</u>?

Evidence for each was covered I think, and I did ask how much she wanted to know. She seemed happy with what I'd said and when I gave her the leaflet as well with the various options.

Negotiation? Hmm, I suppose I spent a lot of time telling her rather than asking what she knew or thought, so the Agreement might not have been so good.

I agree about the evidence and the leaflet was a good idea. Also saw you telling her to take paracetamol and think about physio rather than asking what she felt was best. Sometimes patients make it plain they want you to tell them, but Gran didn't so will she do as you've suggested?

I hope so, but I don't know.

So what might you have done differently?

It's around finding out what she wanted to do isn't it? I need to ask.

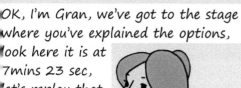

We can see how that goes and you can see one of the doctors in a month or so to report on how it's going.

Worth a try I suppose.

89

So how was that?

Better?

Yes definitely.

Something to think about when you're consulting. It's easier here as we're concentrating on it, much harder when there's everything else going on. Right, I think I've done all I can think of. Are you happy with that?

Yes thanks. I'll get on with my ICEECRENA from now on!

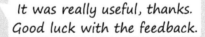

Thanks again for letting me do the tutorial. I enjoyed it, but now I need to see what Tom thinks. See you later.

It was really useful, thanks. Good luck with the feedback.

Here's something to bring up at the WDR 'problems session', after all that denial, Dementia Services have managed to move Madge to a home, the vital question of capacity?

I was looking at the letters yesterday and saw one about a patient I'd sent to Dementia Services with probable vascular dementia and they confirmed that that's what she has.

It wasn't that that made me thin[k] though. It was that she had move[d] into a home and when I saw her i[n] her own house she was really clear she didn't want to move.

I wondered what had happened to get her there. They said something about lacking capacity, but it wasn't clear.

Thanks Aisha, interesting one. Any thoughts?

I struggle with capacity too. We have to consider it a lot, not just when it comes to wills and powers of attorney and this is certainly a good one.

Has she family who can be consulted?

Not that I know of. Her neighbour helped her out before and she didn't know about anyone.

So what do you know about capacity and assessing it?

There's an Act of Parliament on the NHS website about it isn't there?

I'll look it up on here. It's quite complicated and says when people do need to have decisions made for them they must be the least restrictive option.

I suppose that would include moving her to a home if she couldn't be kept safely in her house.

I don't know her well enough to know whether that's the case or not, but it's happened and the Dementia Service deal with this much more often than we do so they'll have taken the Act into account.

I would have thought so. That's a good problem to bring though. Do you think we should look into this in more depth at another session?

Sounds good.

Yeah.

Yes please.

Just been tidying up before leaving. Interesting to read that Dementia Services have moved Madge Moorhouse to a home.

She seemed adamant she was going nowhere. I realised it was unfinished business for me... Intricacies of community care?

We did discuss this at WDR.

Yes, difficult to cope with all that and with austerity developments. Tell you what, let's have tea in the social room, say 4 o'clock?

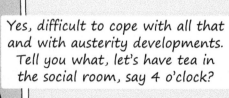

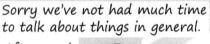

Now, it's the school holidays we can get away.

Sounds like you've been covering it up too...

So, you both really need a break; where are you going?

he Lake District. lly loves walking so we can just relax and talk. Vhat about you? madan's coming up isn't it?

s it is. Some of the fast will be hard when I'm at work, but I've done it before and it doesn't affect my performance. We all come together for Eid and eat too much!

It makes up for the fasting; it's like Christmas so I'm looking forward to that Afterwards I'm going to lie on a beach in Greece with university friends.

Your childhood must have been very different to mine. My family worked in factories and mines 'up north', when there was work. We watched the pennies. Christmas was good but no great feast, and holidays were a bus trip to the coast.

97

Life changes doesn't it? University, reading for pleasure, rugby... another world from home. Lot different now with plenty at Christmas and holidays abroad most years.

Thinking religion, my mother's always found time for the church choir but that's about it for us...

Anyway, home now to Sally!

Let's have a final professional chat tomorrow for this ST year. Same time in my surgery? Meantime, have a think – what's the last four months done for you? Think about the end of year CSR and ESR we did recently.

Can I talk about Frank?

Seems he's got on with that new doctor – he just had to tell me – told her about the lads and trouble AND – just so it doesn't come from someone else – talked to me about Dad and a lot more, but that can wait.

Mum, it's all too much! I'm tired all the time – The doctor calls it 'TATT'... It's all this stress!

What with Laurie being grumpy and staying outside. Told him, if he's going to stay out there and grump, get an allotment! First time he looked me in the eye for ages.

Then there's Tracy. She's applied for a job, but that leaves Millie to be looked after.

Jan love, I can cope with Millie most days.

You can? That's a relief. I've applied for a job in a call centre, but it's only 3 days a week.

I don't know what to do about Frank – I feel really guilty.

Now he's talking, thanks to that doctor, it's getting easier.

He seems quite interested in helping Tracy paint her living room; that could bide him over before the court.

Oh no, he's back, I really can't cope with his moods.

I'll make some tea.

— It wasn't just Gran, I couldn't get pictures of the family she was trying to help out of my mind.

'Staying open to the needs and experience of the patient in the face of one's own motivations and reactions to illness is essentially a psychological task. Modern healthcare policy and guidance makes frequent reference to the notion of working to promote the patient's well being. This concept involves more than symptom management reduction or cure. It is about how the patient is in him/herself and in his/her environment.'

Ballat, J. and Campling, P. (2011) Intelligent Kindness: reforming the culture of healthcare. Cambridge: RCPsych Publications. p. 55.

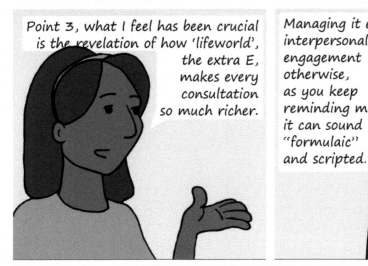

Point 3, what I feel has been crucial is the revelation of how 'lifeworld', the extra E, makes every consultation so much richer.

Managing it effectively needs good interpersonal skills for real patient engagement otherwise, as you keep reminding me, it can sound "formulaic" and scripted.

Good point and I've seen you develop from a 'formulaic' style to be more natural in your consulting.

And if I deserve to return in a year, what do I need to learn in the meantime?

Oh let me think about that... Of course you can return!

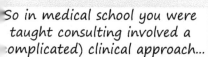

...Still a dominant approach in specialised secondary care.

Now look at this.

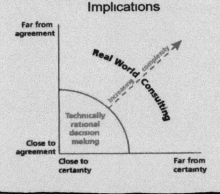

You go from complicated to complex – because of the individuality of patients...

...The big E – a complicated approach would be incomplete in GP, which brings us to the big thrill of GP – uncertainty!

Well, have a great holiday and pop in when you can. I'd love to know how you're getting on at Market Street.

Was that naughty, spoiling Aisha's holiday? Words like complicated and complex have lots of meanings whereas for us doctors it's simple — complicated is what we used to do — find clinical story — make diagnosis — treat. Now we share patients' stories — different every time, and our clinical knowledge, full of ifs and buts and that can be very complex.

It's not just what you say, but what gestures and facial expressions you use.

She'll probably have forgotten about it as the door closed and thoughts of sea and mountains flash into her mind...

'Maintaining curiosity means tolerating ambiguity, expecting the unexpected and welcoming new thoughts — Curiosity's curious influence on medical doctors.'

Werner, A., Rieber, N. and Zipfel, S. (2011) 'Curiosity's curious influence on medical doctors', Medical Education, 45(7). p. 657.

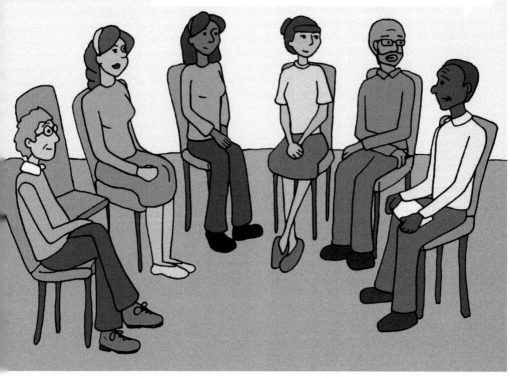

This might be different from other ward rounds.

We discuss each patient's case and then they come in. So, we can plan next stage recovery.

I understand.

How's it going at Awlgate?

It's OK, I suppose... Plenty of time to talk with patients and hear their stories... But, some are so sad

One particularly haunts me...

Hello Namila, I'm Aisha Rashid, or of the doctors here

What happened?

It's hard to talk about.

Yes, I'm sure, clearly very serious. So let's see what we can do as you tell the story.

Mm..m..

Shall I tell yo what I kno from th Accident an Emergenc notes? The you can tell n what bi matte

I see that you tried to hang yourself, but your Mum found you and brought you to A&E — they could see you were upset, but you wouldn't say why.

'ouldn't say anything in front of 1um... It was to do with me and ny boyfriend.

Boyfriend?

You see, he's not Hindu and my family are very strict about that. Do you know what I mean?

Yes, I do understand the difficulty, but was it so bad you wanted to end things?

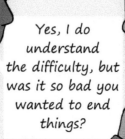

111

I just couldn't see a way out. I really love him, but I love my family too.

Aisha, are you still here?

Oh sorry, I was miles away... Thinking of a case I can relate to.

Anything I can help with?

Oh dear, sorry, but no. It would mean breaking confidentiality and I can't do that. Thanks for offering.

1 MONTH LATER

It's Frank isn't it? I didn't expect to see you here.

Oh it's not me, I'm here to help Jack. He's been right ill with psychosis from the steroids. Getting better now though.

Now I know why you warned me about them when we had a chat some months ago. Ta for that.

You're welcome! How are you doing anyway?

Not so bad now I'm with Gran. She won't stand any nonsense, but she really wants to help. Mum does too, but I can't be near Dad at the moment.

There aren't many people I bond with, but I can't stop talking with Dr Rashid.

'Stressful life experience and symptoms of illness are in constant flux, with symptoms of headache and abdominal pain or palpitations to give just a few of the common examples, being just as likely to be caused by oppressive social conditions or interpersonal strife as by anything that biomedical theory would recognise as disease - - - illness is one of the few valid outlets for human distress'

Heath, I. (2011) 'Divided we Fail', Clinical Medicine, 11(6). p. 578.

It's another world isn't it? OK let's go to our small groups and practise.

We've six SP patients to help during the morning so everyone can have a go.

Yes, and she's much the same, she did have a fall the other day though, which didn't happen last time.

Did she hurt herself?

A bruised forehead and a black eye.

It could be UTI, but she's on Warfarin so I can't rule out a sub-dural.
I'll be round in half an hour so I can have a look at her. Meantime could you dip her urine please?

Thanks Doc, we've some urine sticks here so I'll get her pee checked for when you arrive.

>CLICK<

Thanks Sven, how did that feel?

Good, I wanted to be safe here and couldn't rule out a subdural, so needed to see her.

Morning Jan, what are we looking at today?

It's life I suppose, but things are really getting to me, what with Laurie and his moods, Tracy with her divorce and Frank up in court soon. I don't get a chance to talk with Frank really because he can't stand being around his dad and the feeling's mutual so I hardly see him.

what effect is that having on you and your life?

Well I'm still really tired with not sleeping well, can't stop worrying and I seem to be short with everyone. They've even said things at work... We're short of money and it's all a bit much really...

Hmm, doesn't sound great.

123

So, you're anxious a lot of the time and not sleeping, want to do something about it, but not tablets and it's not so bad that you've thought of harming yourself? — I'm guessing here! Does that sum it up?

Yes, and it's made things clearer for me just talking about it in this way.

So I think what is going on is an understandable anxiety and worries about money. I agree tablets won't be the best here so what about 'talking treatment' where you go through this with a trained worker who can give you some help with managing the anxieties — what we refer to as CBT.

Sounds like it might help and it would be good to talk to someone who's not involved.

As well, have you thought about how you might look for a new job? The library has a job service which might be able to help.

Wow, this is so different from psych — no time to take anything but a basic history and not even that when you're in resus with really sick patients and all you have is the ambulance crew's summary. Even ICE is difficult to find time for, never mind really understanding the patient.

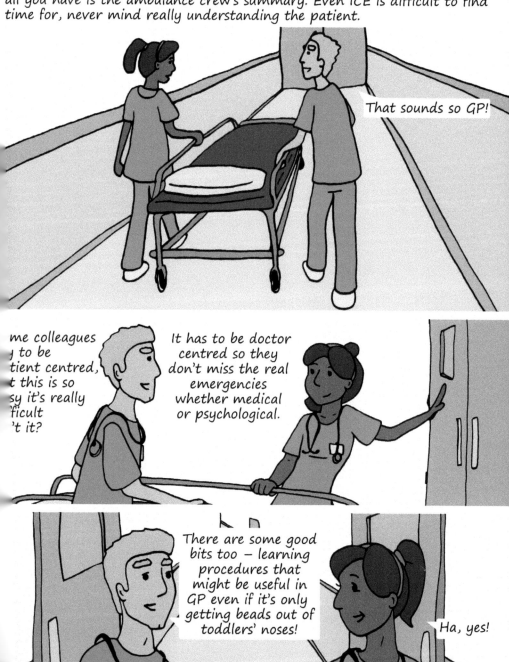

That sounds so GP!

me colleagues
y to be
tient centred,
t this is so
sy it's really
ficult
't it?

It has to be doctor centred so they don't miss the real emergencies whether medical or psychological.

There are some good bits too — learning procedures that might be useful in GP even if it's only getting beads out of toddlers' noses!

Ha, yes!

125

127

128

129

She slipped in the day room a couple of hours ago and caught herself on the arm of a chair as she went down to the floor.

We can't tell what hurts, but something does cos she just shouts out like that.

Can you help me examine her?

Mrs Moorhouse I'm going to have a look at you, is that OK?

Owww!

You know what you were saying about doctor centred consulting? I think I've just had the most doctor centred session as the poor patient was demented and could only say "Owww" and it got louder when I found her broken ribs.

Well, I suppose it could be seen as patient centred. You did what she needed even if she couldn't tell you much.

Suppose? She is someone from my practic so I knew a little of how she'd been a I've seen her deteriorate even in t short time I' known h

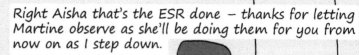

Right Aisha that's the ESR done — thanks for letting Martine observe as she'll be doing them for you from now on as I step down.

Can I say though I'm really impressed with your AKT result...

One of the best we've seen, but I was aware you knew your stuff!

Especially whilst tackling some busy and difficult jobs — never mind having to see your trainer's wife.

Well, that wasn't easy, but far worse for the two of you by a long way.

Mmm, I really do have to cut down here — there's always the pressure to work but also mindful of the GMC requiring you to be well enough to do so.

Don't worry Tom, we all understan and want you to have the best possible time with Sally for... as lor as you can.

We'll be OK with your training won't we Aisha?

I agree it's important you can give all your thoughts to Sally and not us and the patients.

Thanks — on a brighter note, what do you think you'll get from your time at Market Street?

'm hoping I'll see a wider range of eople than here because they have more mobile population and a vider mix f ethnic ackgrounds.

Not to mention income differences. I love the stability here and being able to see people through things, but I need to know about other ways of practising Primary Care.

All good points and I hope it pays off — finish your A&E and you'll have experienced an additional range of medical and social problems.

Then back here for a year — I'm really looking forward to that.

137

This is what we call our Education Room, you'll see we occupy an old school building.

AFTER THE MEETING

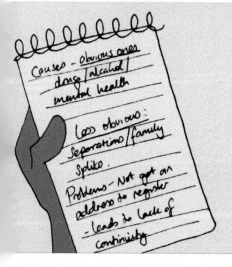

What would I do differently? Now knowing what could happen - so getting help soonest from drug and alcohol services or Shelter. There is a homeless service here in the city...

I'll have to check that for Jupiter Road - I'll put that down as a future learning need. Oh dear, what do I put down about mental health issues?

DAYS LATER

Chandrika Mistry - everyone calls me Chan. I suppose you know quite a bit about diabetes?

Yes, but I'm not sure yet, as to how it's dealt with in GP.

Ok, let's get started, we ca talk as we go

t's mostly routine checks for blood and ensation tests, making sure they're OK vith meds — diet and exercise of course and for new cases getting them onto an education rogramme.

So Mrs Patel everything is going well I think — glucose-HbA1c and oods stable and you're happy with he tablets, so I'll see you in a year unless anything else crops up meantime.

_ There was a point when Mrs Patel said something and the daughter said something different — it doesn't matter in terms of her condition, but it does make me wonder about interpreters.

now, Language Line is better in ne ways, as you know what's being d, but family members are more ilable and patients more comfortable.

Suppose I'm lucky because I understand some Hindi and Urdu. It just highlights the difference between translating and interpreting — how patient-centred can you be if you don't know the difference between what a patient says and what they've been told to say?

Afternoon.

Afternoon Mr Chaudhry. Take a seat.

The eye screening has indicated we might need a check-up?

Yeah, wife made me go, I heard some muttering at the test but there's no need.

When did you last have a blood-glucose test?

Look, it was s months ago be so what. I'm fi and whatever my tests hav been OK for years!

That may be so, but over the years tests vary, that's why more regular tests are needed.

Come off it. That's not what Google says.

Depends where you look. There's lots of info, not all of it right.

What I'm about to say is well wo thinking about. With your conditi and age there are risks to heart, eyes and legs, as you probably know AND as years go by you might not be aware of them until it's too late. The eye screening has caused concern...

I suggest you have some tests today, now. What do you say?

Can I come back tomorrow?
Can I be sure you will?
I suppose so, what time?

I'll squeeze you in at 9:30 OK?

144

Look, it was six months ago but so what. I'm fine and whatever, my tests have been OK for years!

'The patient and the physician play distinct roles in medical decision making. The physician is usually the first to recommend a particular course of action and thus in a position that we call decisional priority, a phrase that is meant to imply antecedence but not superiority. The competent adult patient, who reaps the rewards or suffers the consequences of any intervention, retains final decisional authority, an authority that is delegated to family or surrogate when the patient cannot make decisions.'

Whitney, S. N., McGuire, A. L. and McCullough, L. B. (2004) 'A Typology of Decision-making, Informed Consent and Simple Consent', Annals of Internal Medicine 140(1). p. 54.

The next patient is Gujarati, from India via Uganda from a local suburb where there's a lot of diabetes but she speaks English better than me.

Probably me too, and I know about the genetic risks. It's why I run in my spare time.

WEEK LATER

It's been quite an insight here after a suburban practice, so glad I've had an induction, Chan was really helpful about chronic care in diabetes...

...how it overlaps with hypertension and IHD for example and she's so quick.

Yes, she's gre... doesn't oft... get stuck b... knows when... call us Ready to st... on yo... own no...

LATER

So I've, er, lost my prescription – right?

Mmm, so wh... prescriptio... was that?

It's me mefadone. The drug worker said not to miss doses

Ok but tell me how it got lost.

Must've slipped out of me pocket on the bus...

...So I need more.

Not sure about this, it was only done yesterday.

So, gor... do i... wh...

147

Andrew is a difficult one, isn't he?

You can say that again, didn't know what to say or do, glad you told me where the panic button is. He went very meek and mild with you though.

We go back a long way. So what have you learnt apart from where the panic button is?

Think I need to learn more about drug addiction and its management. I'll put that in my e-Portfolio. Not much I can say about patient centred care.

Good plan about being more aware, any ideas how?

Attending the Drug Worker Clinic?

Great idea, we have a lot of drug issues here, but it's probably more hidden in suburbia. As for patient centred care, there are occasions when you can't really do it because this is about patient NEEDS, not what they WANT.

So, with our Jyoti and Priti already there that will be 4 children off to school from our two houses!

It might make sense for us to share collecting them, I could go with one of you for three days a week?

Sounds good, I'll need to find out what flexibility I have at work.

Is that Rupal?

LATER

153

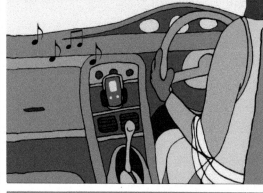

Aisha it's Martine, are you driving?

Yeah but it's hands free.

I've some news, best if you pull up.

I didn't want you distracted when I tell you that Sally's died.

Oh... What happened?

It was all very peaceful – she'd been in there a week or two until she just drifted off – Tom's OK as you might expect, but the funeral's next Thursday and I hoped you could come seeing as how you and Sally got on and how you helped them both at Christmas in A&E. I'm going too so if you like we could meet at the practice and go together?

Yes it's so sad – I hate funerals, but knowing Sally and appreciating how helpful Tom's been with me, I really do want to go. Thursday's my study day and WDR so I can miss them for once.

155

Thanks for coming, I do appreciate the support.

No problem, it was a lovely ceremony.

We talked a lot and that's what Sally wanted, so I think she would have approved.

Are you both coming back to the house?

Martine's brought me from the surgery so I'm with her.

Yes we can come back Tom, I'm not on duty, see you there.

We've a few more people to talk to, but then we'll be on our way. The caterers are managing arrival before we get there so you won't be hanging about dripping.

156

157

I wanted to get your advice first.

'Lest we forget, for countless patients it is the telling of their stories that helps make them well.'

Glyn Elwyn, Richard Gwyn – Stories we hear and stories we tell: analyzing talk in GP, BMJ/318 – 1999

MARKET STREET EDUCATION ROOM

Joint tutorial today. Aisha's told me she's still keen on being a GP so that's why I've asked Dr Imtiaz to join us as well as Jack, our STI registrar, to consider Patient Centred Care in different cultural settings.

Yes, "is it appropriate to stick to ICEE" has often gone through my mind, as well as the underlying concordance approach of CRENA.

Particularly when the patient says "well you're the doctor".

Fair enough but how do you deal with that?

I find it's similar in some parts of Europe and the Middle East where the older generation think you have to decide for them.

My relatives in Pakistan think that the doctor should know everything and if you don't give them a pill, or better still an injection, you're no good and they don't come back.

So, does being patient-centred necessarily mean you share decisions with those patients?

No, especially if they are grey, sweaty and complaining of central chest pain which is almost certainly a heart attack and you say, well we have some options here:

...we could get a 999 ambulance or we could leave you here and see if you die.

159

Seriously though it's also not right if the patient wants to tell you what to do. It's the in between patients who're the hardest, but in today's sense of patients who are not used to NHS ways of working there's no harm in explaining how we are expected to share thinking — hoping that it will help next time they come.

Can I ask something?

Of course, ask away.

We are taught about ICEE in medical school, but are there easier ways to get what you want?

A very good question. Two things come to mind but putting it into practice harder than knowing it. The first is, just letting the patient tell you, just listening and not interrupting too early, when I watch videos of myself I see that the patient has told me part of the ICEE without me asking — th second is explaining why you are asking — something like "I've a few idea: about what's happening, but wonder what you think and whether you've talked to others about the symptoms or had thoughts about things you'd li me to rule in or out".

Ah that makes sense — I've seen Dr Mac do tha sort of thing a few times but not twigged why.

It took me a time to see that happening!

Any other issues?

There are other issues such as aspects of translation and interpretation, dealing with family members telling you what to do for the patient and use of chaperones but I've always been helped by colleagues over coffee with those problems, so thank you but not for today.

That's great but you raise an interesting problem that Dr Imtiaz might have that we don't.

Jack, have you seen "Victoria and Abdul"?

No?

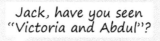

OK, well what I was thinking about is a very traditional female patient seeing a male Dr, needing abdomen exam and not wanting him to do it? What would he have to do? Think about it and we'll talk later.

Aisha, I think it would help Jack if you tell her how helpful Chan has been out treating diabetics, and finally — I know you are going on a yoga holiday before your last three weeks here and we may not have the chance to say how pleased we've been to have you here and wish you all the best for your ST3 year.

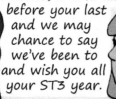

163

164

Hi Gran, thanks for letting me know about the vacancy at Jupiter Road. Really glad you saw that advert in the waiting room. I've got the job!

That's great our Tracy, when do you start?

Luckily, I've no job to leave – they're keen to have me, so I start next week. Really interesting too; it's about helping patients coming home from hospital. Because of my legal and mediation training they also want my help with any complaints.

They don't get many, but when they do I can use my mediation skills.

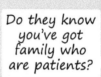

Do they know you've got family who are patients?

Yes, I told them it was you who spotted the ad – but obviously someone else will have to mediate if it's one of our lot involved.

Well we certainly won't be complaining given the help we've had recently.

No, that's good, anyway, thought I'd tell you first before I ring Mum. Thanks again! Love you.

165

Good to have you here again. There's a few changes since before. Now Tom's left I've become senior partner and you'll be working alongside two newcomers who'll extend our cover.

With patients you mean?

First there's Pratika our pharmacist who'll deal with complex medications directly with patients. She's part-time here.

And there's Tra who'll liaise wi the Integrate Locality Tear involved wi patients makir quicker journe from hospital home, about whi more later. An added bonus that Tracy is legal trained she might be helpful in oth ways. She's been given t role of complaints offic

And this is your key year for your CCT so we'll be looking at the joy of dealing with complexity and what follows on from ICEE.

You didn't even blink!

I'm speechless.

Welcome back!

Our paths have crossed, but I don't suppose you knew what I was up to. Now we'll be talking medication reviews. I'm so pleased I've got into Primary Care helping patients still feel there's continuity of care.

OK let's have the details.

I've done medication reviews at Market Street, but you review all chronically ill patients here, do you?

That's right; some weren't sure when I started because I'm not a doctor, but I have the time to check - are they taking the agreed dose? Got a system to take all their pills? Take them regularly or not? – or just not bothered, they may tell me but not their doc. It's more difficult when they've lost the plot and need help.

I can see we're into a whole new layer of patient care. Not before time. I remember opening a cupboard under the sink of an older patient and there was 20 years of pill boxes, some never opened, some still half full.

169

Fascinating, first of all I must compliment you on the consistent way you responded to such a variety of patient conditions. Talking as an equal, sharing.

I'll confess my agenda was to look specifically at your use of interpersonal skills. You've got the 'Consulting Expertise Paper' haven't you?

First of all, greeting patient, as we said before, years ago almost every GP would say 'what can I do for you today?' No more. The 'I' sets up an 'I'm the expert consultation so limiting for patients at a time when we want them to share aspects of their 'lifeworld' so important for future patient care. The Syrian mother was puzzled; why did you want to know about living conditions and immunisation rather than just give her medicine for her baby's wheeze? You smiled and explained why it was important to understand any background factors for an informed diagnosis given there might be different cultural expectations.

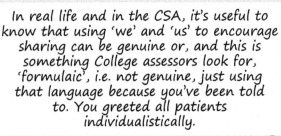

In real life and in the CSA, it's useful to know that using 'we' and 'us' to encourage sharing can be genuine or, and this is something College assessors look for, 'formulaic', i.e. not genuine, just using that language because you've been told to. You greeted all patients individualistically.

On the list you will see columns for skills and behaviours. Skills identify what you are using whereas behaviours show how you are using them. Let me explain: signalling is an important skill i.e. explaining what you are about to do, but if your tone of voice is uninterested and you are engrossed with the computer screen the patient might not even listen. Eye contact and tone of voice connect the skill with the necessary behaviour.

Empathy-wise I've written examples for all five cases with good rapport. You did classic risks, evidence, negotiation and agreement with the rugby player despite his embarrassment that his shoulder injury was a result of boozing and not a rugby injury. And when you summarised an agreed conclusion with the bus driver he said how helpful it had been to understand the background to his sleeplessness and the daily worry about heart palpitation possibly resulting in a crash as happened in Glasgow. Something to talk about with his mates.

I could list other skills witnessed, but I think you are nearly at the point where you can be at ease facing a full range of patient conditions AND OK to apply for CSA this October.

Otherwise I think the Antiguan woman felt an affinity with you, the TATT woman was somewhat relieved to discuss her husband's aggression. A good afternoon!

Thanks that's really helpful.

Inevitably a lot of the first part of this year has been concentrating on the CSA.

'I have never entirely escaped the view that being a doctor is something of a moral luxury, by which doctors are easily corrupted. We can easily end up complacent and self important, feeling ourselves to be more important than our patients.' – p31

'There is nothing more frightening for a patient than a doctor, especially a young one, who is lacking in confidence. Furthermore, patients want hope, as well as treatment.' – p244

Marsh, H. (2017) Admissions: A life in Brain Surgery. London: Weidenfield and Nicolson.

175

This job's changed my life, difficult to get to grips with, but lots of people to chat with. It's opened up things for me – people running food banks in their spare time, others studying...

Grandad!

Sounds like another world, mine's all children at the moment but I often think, what am I to do when they're all at school? A part-time job sounds great.

Has Gran told you about Frank? He's loving his community work, says he wants to study horticulture. What a change in him.

That's great news.

Let's go home Millie.

Thanks for looking after her Mum.

Is Dad ok? I must have been hiding when he was having a go at Frank...

He's still not right.

Complications!

'John The first feature of these Happy Valley Folk is their basic positive and friendly attitude; the second is their degree of emotional independence, ...
...the third is family structure...
...the next is the family's free and open communication...
...the fifth is their ability to perceive the world very clearly...
...and finally they can cope very readily with change that would floor the rest of us...
Robin ..that pretty well covers the main points.
John You know I suddenly had a mental picture of all our readers staring at the ceiling, thinking, "who on earth do I know like who's like that?"
Robin Well how many Olympic Gold Medallists do you know?
John OK. Now to put what you've been saying into perspective, I want you to compare this very healthy family behaviour with both typical mid-range behaviour, and with positively unhealthy behaviour.'

Life and how to survive it R Skinner and J Cleese BCA London 1993 p35

Panel 1

I think you've seen this complaint haven't you?

Yes, he's upset and I'm upset, he thinks I let him down.

It's not just you. He's mentioned others for not telling him about the risk of bone thinning from the tablets he takes for his arthritis.

So he's feeling badly treated. What do we do about it?

Panel 2

Well I'm still feeling my way into th kind of medical complaint, first to find out what happened and then reply. Show we care. My advice is to ask him in and discuss it. Your indemnity organisation will help you to make a suitable reply, but please show it to me so I can learn.

To be honest I just didn't think of the inappropriate position I was putting him in. I'm stressed about it now though.

Panel 3

Oh I know all about stress, how do you deal with it?

Running helps me a lot.

Panel 4

Maybe I should take that u

Why don't you come to the park on Sunday morning? There's a gentle run you can try.

If I can leave Millie with Gran, I'll be there.

Meantime I'll get this sorted.

Glad you're taking it seriously, all those ladies looking at me at the bloomin' Menopause Clinic!

I can imagine the embarrassment. We're sorry we hadn't spotted the need for a scan and arranged it at the rheumatology clinic.

Yes, sorry, I should have foreseen the problem.

ll that would have been better. eally wanted to make sure you realised what you'd done so you wouldn't put another innocent soul in that situation.

We've discussed this as a whole practice so even those who don't know you are aware of what can happen, so thanks for letting us know about it.

Well then I suppose that's it?

We're happy to draw a line under it if that's OK with you, but you could take it further if you wish.

You've obviously learnt from it so I'm happy to let it lie. At least the scan showed I was alright for now... ...and it's worth a pint when I tell the story at the pub tonight. They'll have a right giggle at my expense!

183

Thank you Mr Oxley.

How do you feel after that?

Could be better. I'm upset, having a complaint and worse still, it's a reasonable one.

Mmm... well complaints are hard, but if you learn from them you can be positive. After all the NHS is a no blame culture organisation. We're learning all the time, hopefully!

Ready for today's session? Looking at another video aren't we?

Yes, I did this one yesterday afternoon so the cases are fresh in my mind.

Good, any thoughts on what to look at?

ot really, I'm too involved with getting ready for CSA to think of anything else. Assessment's a bit differently focussed isn't it?

Good point, let's look at CRENA in more depth shall we? It'll help with day to day consulting as well as CSA.

Fine, I can remember most of CRENA but the 'A'.

Agreement. Funny, when concordance/CRENA was first highlighted some research showed that most GPs never got as far as agreement, they seemed to focus more on the E for evidence.

ut it's the whole point of the exercise isn't it?

This is Mr F. He's a atient I've seen before when he wanted to crease his tramadol.

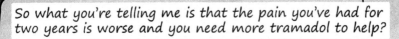

So what you're telling me is that the pain you've had for two years is worse and you need more tramadol to help?

Yes please Doc, it's really stopping me doing anything much now.

OK, I'd like to talk about this medication to see if there's another way to help, because I'm concerned there might be a problem with the tramadol.

It's not a problem for me.

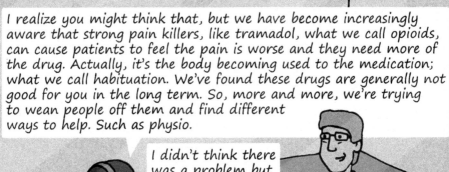

I realize you might think that, but we have become increasingly aware that strong pain killers, like tramadol, what we call opioids, can cause patients to feel the pain is worse and they need more of the drug. Actually, it's the body becoming used to the medication; what we call habituation. We've found these drugs are generally not good for you in the long term. So, more and more, we're trying to wean people off them and find different ways to help. Such as physio.

I didn't think there was a problem but you're right, I'm taking more than when I started.

I need practice for this!

Have you heard of the app Couch to 5K, it might help?

Never mind that, where's the coffee shop? Then I'd better get home to save Gran from Millie.

So how was your run?

It was good, but difficult being friends with someone whose family I know well from work. What if I let something confidential slip?

I can see that, but if you work in an area you will always have that sort of dilemma. Just be aware, that's all you can do.

How are you anyway? After the complaint I mean.

A bit bruised actually, the patient was nice when we saw him, but I should have thought more widely AND didn't like being in the spotlight.

Yeah, my trainer says it's something we all have to face from time to time no matter how hard we try to do the right thing.

189

Ambulance please!

What happened?

I'm sorry Mrs Carter, he was very poorly when he got here and we couldn't do anything to help.

It looks like he had a stroke and that's why he came off his bike.

I just don't understand, he'd been more active recently, back and forth to the allotment on his bike, he was even a bit less grumpy.

Mmm, he was unlucky, a mini-stroke like he's had, does increase the risk of something worse. From what you say it sounds like he was doing things right. Many are OK for years but unfortunately not your Laurie...

193

Not everything in life goes the way you think it will or want it to does it?

'Medicine used to be simple, effective and relatively safe. It is now complex, effective and potentially dangerous. The mystical authority of the doctor used to be essential for practice. Now we need to be open and work in partnership with our colleagues in health care and with our patients' (quote from Cyril Chantler).

Leng, G. et al (2017) 'National Commitment to shared decision making: The only way to achieve truly person centred care', BMJ 359, p. j4746.

195

We really did start anywhere and I think I managed to go there.

After a big silence she said,

'I'm so lonely'.

The days seem to go on forever so I have drink for something to d

I suppose that's why I'm here.

Yes?

Well the family found some empties in the compost heap and told me to get help.

But what about the loneliness, is that the real point?

Yes, but it's a bit mo complicat because son in l. is stron, an alcol

He had refused to let my grand-daughter Louise visit me. I'd wondered why.

So, I thought I'd really go somewhere with her by discussing whether he would agree to see the Drug and Alcohol Team and we agreed to make another appointment to talk about the loneliness. I did 'safety net' as well by telling her not to stop outright in order to reduce the risk of things like seizures.

Excellent, you did fit the patient's part, doctor's part and shared part, didn't you? Any others?

Oh Yes. I've been keeping this till last, are you sitting comfortably? Well, in comes Mrs Solanki who's next door neighbour to the Carters with a man I guess is her husband.

He confidently draws up a chair by Mrs S and takes over, 'Mrs S wants your advice about the behaviour of her 9 year old son Kitesh. 'Hang on', I say and look at Mrs S and say, 'why can't I speak to you?', 'I've no idea' she says in perfect English, 'I've never seen this man before today. He came up to me in the waiting room and asked me why I was here in Gujarati. I thought he was another patient'.

So I look at the man who says, I'm just a translator, they asked for me because they didn't think Dr Rashid would speak Gujarati. I burst out laughing as did Mrs S. It turned out there was an apprentice on the Reception Desk when Mrs Solanki registered as a new patient: he'd just filled in the form without clarifying anything.

For the record, Daksha, as she insisted I call her, wanted advice about son Kitesh possible autism. She mentioned sufficient symptoms for me to arrange an appointment with a specialist.

First, I think I need a serious word with Reception. And hearing about Carter's neighbour reminds me. Tracy will be back next week. I wonder how the family is adjusting? – However we're finished now.

Before you go. Nurse called me in. Had a patient who'd tripped on the pavement while on her phone. Seriously grazed heel of palm but she wanted a second opinion on what turned out to be bits of phone in the wound. Just thought you would like to know, as we've been saying how long before we start to get phone induced injuries. It's happened!

Better add to my e-Portfolio. I'm told to be self-reflective... Two patients, one wanted pills the other didn't... Mr Crowther with a 24 hour BP recording of 150/95, a fit, non-smoker who didn't want tablets. OK but I thought he needed some guidelines, so, we looked at NHS guidelines. He didn't like possible side effects of various tablets. He'd already started lifestyle changes so we agreed he'd concentrate on those and come back in three months – so what have I learnt?

-**C**hoices
-**R**isks
-**E**vidence
-**N**egotiation
-**A**greement

CRENA can happen in normal consultation time – and conversationally! |

And then Mrs Bingly; wanted antibiotics for a two day cough, wasn't otherwise unwell, clear chest, non-smoker but here ICEE came into play. Her Concern was messing up her daughter's wedding the next day and Expectation was that antibiotics would work by tomorrow.

So, sympathetically suggesting warm drinks would help for the wedding day, even if I had evidence she had a bacterial infection, which she hadn't, resulted in her thanking me for being so caring, so sharing conversations succeeded in both contrasting cases.

I'll add, tone of voice and eye contact probably helped.

What else did I learn and how am I going to manage that? Hmm...

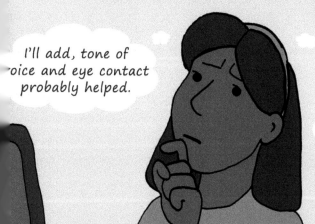

So, assessments completed; CCT applied for, got a job. Now to learn what being a GP is really like!

Family practice in Britain is a rushed, unglamorous life and the effects of its heavy workload can be grinding and corrosive. Yet, for all of this, I think there's a quiet and unacknowledged heroism about it all. And it may well be one of the last survivors (though not the only one) of a long tradition of 'real' medicine, the type of holistic approach to health care that has always tried to treat the person as well as their disease, and to do this within the context of their own home, their family and their community.

Helman, C. (2006) Suburban Shaman: tales from medicine's frontline. London: Hammersmith Press. pp. 2-3.

--- Every day I see the value in taking a whole person view of health. Yes, I must think scientifically and analytically to make clinical diagnoses. But generalists don't just think of you as a body part that's gone wrong - we try to see the whole of you. Your family, your views, your history, your hopes, your worries. And we are with you for the whole journey from cradle to grave. With more people growing older, often living with several long term conditions and lists of medications, someone needs to be keeping an eye on the big picture and helping you navigate through an increasingly complex health system.

Easton, G. (2016) The Appointment: What your doctor really thinks during your 10-minute consultation. London: Robinson. p. X.

So Frank, how are you?

Good thanks Doc. Better than I've been for ages. I'm off all that stuff, court's sorted and I've got a job.

Don't laugh, but I'm even on an RHS training course.

Wow that's great.

Sorry about your dad.

I'm not. I know I should be, but he's the reason I got into so much trouble.

How come?

Well, I've never talked about it, but he never liked me and everything I did was wrong.

A LITTLE LATER

From what you and your mum told me and from what I've found looking at you and your wee, Millie, I'm pretty sure you haven't got appendicitis, this is good.

Not so good is that the pain is going to be there for a few more days because it's a problem called mesenteric adenitis. Funny word, but it means there are glands up inside your tummy due to a virus and that's hurting.

They'll settle so all you need is some paracetamol that Mum can give you when you rest for a few days.

OK, thank you.

You're welcome young lady, get well soon.

Thanks Doctor, I'm relieved it's not appendicitis.

No, I'm pretty sure it isn't but if Millie gets worse not better and particularly if the pain's mostly here then see someone urgently.

So a final shared surgery, what do you want to look at today?

Well I'm conscious that interpersonal skills are a constant and constantly variable in the way they need to be used.

Agreed, we know you can do the data gathering as we've seen here and confirmed by the CSA result. The same with clinical management and, to be perfectly honest, your interpersonal skills are good too but fluency in that is key to expert consulting.

Can we look at that then?

I'll select two of today's list that might test that out.

So Sara, Mum's brought you because you won't go to school, she's tried to persuade you and now thinks we might help. What's behind all this?

Dunno.

I really want to help if I can, but you don't seem keen to talk. Would it help if Mum sat outside for a while?

Would you mind? Sometimes it's easier this way.

Is it any easier to talk now?

Well, I'm pretty sure there's a reason for not wanting to go to school and one thing I spotted in your notes is that you've had a difficult time for the past two years.

kaay, if u think will help.

Dunno.

Well I noticed you lost your Dad, must have been horrible.

It was, still is.

Still is?

Yeah, everyone at school does things as a family or even just with their dads and I can't.

I can't even get away from it when I'm not at school 'cos they post the great things they're doing. I just want to hide under the duvet.

Yeah, I get that, I'm sure I'd be the same.

I just miss him so, I can't talk about him to Mum 'cos she gets all upset, she's not really let him go either.

211

Come in Mr Bond. I've got Dr Proctor sitting in with me if that's ok?

OK Doc.

Hello Barry, try and ignore me today, Dr Rashid's in charge.

So what are we doing today Mr Bond?

Call me Barry, everyone does. I just need a letter please.

Mmm, letter?

Yes please, my daughter needs a letter for her employers so she can have a week's leave to look after me whilst my wife has an operation.

That's unusual, can you explain a bit more?

You might have noticed got Parkinson's and I c get very unstea on my pir Joyce usu gets me wh fall, she's this op and won' able to for a week o

So Pat's offered to come and stay as she has for the odd day before, but her boss want a doctor's letter to confirm she's up front about it. Apparently they've had load of lead-swingers so have come up with this plan to sort out the sheep from the goats if you follow me.

Yeah, I think so, it's the first time I've ever been asked for this kind of thing, usually we charge for letters unless they are referrals, will the company pay?

Doubt they'r a load skinflin I'll pa thoug

Sorry to interrupt but, given the circumstances, and your other chronic problems we'll not charge.

Thanks, but really I don't mind paying, Joyce might cancel her op if Pat can't come.

, no, if Dr Proctor says it's OK let's just do it. You need to confirm that you need help provided by your daughter. I can't say anything about your wife without her being ere or giving written consent as it will breaking confidentiality regarding her.

By the way, I'll be generalising your condition in order to limit problems regarding your confidentiality.

I understand and am very grateful.

, I'm running late as you know so if it's alright, do the letter later if you will pick it up.

That's fine Doc, we only live round the corner and I need the exercise, that's providing I don't fall over in the process!

, before I go, you mind cking this me as ll Doc?

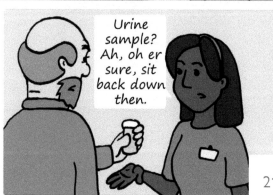

Urine sample? Ah, oh er sure, sit back down then.

215

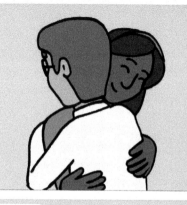

Tom!

So you are staying on? That's great news!

How do you see things going?

Well, I really need to start understanding GP, it's a bit like driving, I'll know more when I'm on my own!

Yes, and such an interesting time, lots of changes in the NHS and Primary Care with Foundations, Networks and wider work in the community; never mind the medicine.

I know, I need to start understanding all these things and the way genetics is going, it'll be a whole new world. It's one thing knowing that certain blood pressure meds are best in different ethnic groups or ages, but when we can tailor treatment to each person, 'personalised medicine', ooh.

Quite, it'll be different, but you'll still need your ICEE CRENA and to understand people and find ways to make sure they have continuity of care.

Ice-cream?

No it's an acronym for things to do in consultation.

I'll bore you with it later but for now let's enjoy the party!

CONSULTING EXPERTISE
Interpersonal Language for Medical Communication

SKILLS

QUESTIONING
Open- closed- circular- echo- **probing**

LISTENING
Hearing- acknowledging- use of silence-

RESPONDING
Affirming – NSPN*

INFORMING
Sequencing- use of lay language

SIGNALLING
Sharing interview process

SUMMARISING
Used mid consultation or as conclusion

EMPATHISING
Entering patient's state of mind

NON-VERBAL
Demeanour- voice tone - eye contact

* Non-specific professional noise

SKILLED BEHAVIOURS

Greeting

Establishing Rapport

Recognising cues & clues

Eliciting disclosure

Maintaining rapport

'Going there'

Informing

Checking understanding

Negotiating

Reassuring

Prioritising - Parking

DEVELOPMENT OF CONSULTING EXPERTISE

PATIENT CENTRED CONSULTING LEARNING JOURNEY

Basic Principles

Starting the consultation

ESTABLISH MUTUALITY
* Replace 'what can I do for you?' with 'what do we need to do today?'

RESPOND INDIVIDUALISTICALLY
* Be prepared to consider the personal together with the medical

EMPOWER THE PATIENT
* Enable the patient to take control when appropriate

More practically

WELCOME PATIENT INITIATIVE
* Allow the consultation to go in unanticipated directions

TEST THE IMPACT OF DIFFERENT INTERPERSONAL SKILLS
* Use the full range of interpersonal skills

USE AND PERSONALISE FRAMEWORKS
* E.g. explore the application of ICEE (Ideas – Concerns – Expectations - Effects)

WORK TOWARDS ACHIEVING CONCORDANCE
* Develop mutuality of treatment using CRENA
(Choices - Risks - Evidence - Negotiation - Agreement)

SAFETY-NET
* Check security of agreed treatment

Be aware

* You will often be dealing with UNCERTAINTY
* SOCIAL and CULTURAL DIVERSITY can affect the consultation
so recognise and share patient language and culture when appropriate
* USE OF TIME will always be a problem

Look forward to meeting patients professionally *at ease* after RCGP acceptance

IDEAS FOR FURTHER READING

Ballat, J. and Campling, P. (2011) Intelligent Kindness: reforming the culture of healthcare. Cambridge: RCPsych Publications.

Barry, C. et al (2001) 'Giving voice to the lifeworld. More humane, more effective medical care? A qualitative study of doctor–patient communication in general practice', Social Science & Medicine, 53 (4), pp. 487-505.

Bradford VTS (2019) Aloba Guide --121 -- detailed.pdf. Available at: https://www.bradfordvts.co.uk/wp-content/onlineresources/communication-skills/teach-communication-skills/aloba/aloba%20guide%20-%20121%20-%20detailed.pdf (Accessed 25/04/20).

Groene, R. et al (2017) 'The health literacy dyad: the contribution of future GPS in England', Education for Primary Care, 28 (5), pp. 274-281.

Hawthorne, K., Roberts, C. and Atkins, S. (2017) 'Sociolinguistic factors affecting performance in the Clinical Skills Assessment of the MRCGP: a mixed methods approach', British Journal of General Practice, 1 (1), pp. 1-9.

Kurtz, S., Silverman, J. D. and Draper, J. (2004) Teaching and Learning Communication Skills in Medicine (second edition) Oxford: Radcliffe Publishing.

NHS Choices (2018) Mental Capacity Act? Available at: https://www.nhs.uk/conditions/social-care-and-support-guide/making-decisions-for-someone-else/mental-capacity-act/ (Accessed: 25/04/20).

Pendleton, D., Schofield, T., Tate, P. and Havelock, P. (1984) The consultation: an approach to learning and teaching. Oxford: Oxford University Press.

Pendleton, D., Schofield, T., Tate, P. and Havelock, P (2003) The new consultation. Oxford: Oxford University Press.

Radford, R. and Johnson, S. (2015) NHS don't kill me! Kibworth Beauchamp: Matador Publishing.

Sackett, D. L. et al (1996) 'Evidence based medicine: what it is and what it isn't', BMJ, 312 (71), pp. 71-72.

Worrall, P., French, A. and Ashton, L. (eds) (2009) Advanced Consulting in Family Medicine: The Consultation Expertise Model. Oxford: Radcliffe Publishing.